11+
English
Spelling & Vocabulary

Intermediate Level
WORKBOOK 6

Dr Stephen C Curran

with Warren Vokes

Edited by Mark Schofield

This book belongs to

Accelerated Education Publications Ltd.

proper	property	consist
conduct	damage	voyage
advantage	wages	silent
parent	absent	serpent

Exercise 116a

1) Their employer paid their __wages__ on the Thursday of each week.

2) The _____ tempted Eve with an apple in the Garden of Eden.

3) The safety _____ in the theatre was lowered during the interval.

4) The lost _____ comprised everything from an umbrella to a set of dentures.

5) They were relieved to sight land after such a long and dangerous _____ .

6) The flames had been dowsed quickly but the _____ was still considerable.

7) She had put an extra _____ on the bed in case it got colder during the night.

8) The club chairman's death was marked by a minute's _____ before the game.

9) Jewish families worship at a synagogue every _____ .

10) The consent form had to be signed by a _____ or guardian. **Score** ⬜ 10

Exercise 116b

11) It was a _____ act of bravery and he was awarded the Victoria Cross.

12) The bishop, dressed in his _____ robe and carrying a crosier, led the procession.

13) He is taller than his rivals and has a distinct _____ in the high jump event.

14) They were told to wear _____ hiking boots and no other type of footwear.

15) His _____ during the lesson was unacceptable and he was given detention.

16) The millionaire agreed to _____ the expedition with all its equipment.

17) His breakfast used to _____ of eggs and bacon but nowadays he eats cereal.

18) The car is powered by an electric motor and is virtually _____ in operation.

19) She was _____ from school because she was suffering from influenza.

20) They tried everything to _____ the spread of the disease. **Score** ⬜ 10

2

Across

116

1. To carry out, manage, or control something.
2. Appropriate or correct.
3. Provide and install furniture and other fittings.
5. Long journey by sea or air.
6. Colour combining red and blue.
9. To be made up of something.
14. Just reward or recompense.

Across (continued)

15. Mother or father.
17. Stop something from taking place.
18. A superior or favourable position.

Down

1. Cloth hung to cover something.
4. Utterly quiet.
6. Something of value that is owned.
7. Worth noticing or commenting on.
8. Physical harm or injury.
10. Quietness.
11. A snake.
12. Sixth day of the week.
13. Large piece of thick cloth used as a cover for a bed.
16. Not present.

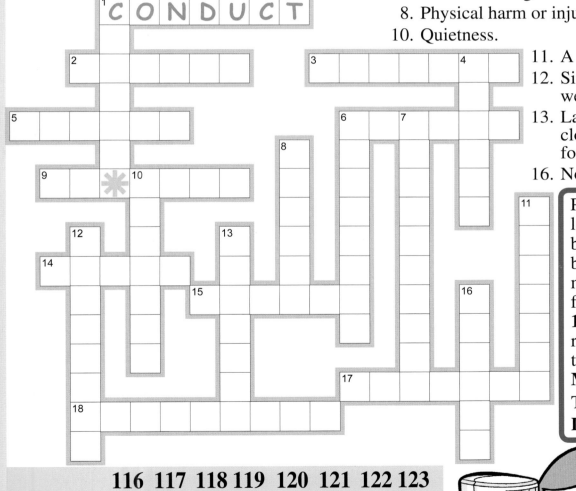

Put the mystery letter (✱) into the box marked **116** below. Add in the mystery letters from puzzles **117** to **123**, then rearrange them to make **Kate's Mystery Word**. The clue is **DRINK**.

	116	117	118	119	120	121	122	123
Enter your mystery letters here:								

Now rearrange them:

Mystery Word:

Score

20

former	organ	orchard
coward	also	almost
already	always	murder
altogether	although	comfort

Across

117

1. Notwithstanding that.
5. By or at an earlier time than expected.
6. A warning device.
10. Not exactly, not yet, or not in fact, but very close to being or happening as described.
11. Area of fruit or nut trees.
15. To gather a crop.
17. Possibly, or it may be.
18. Somebody lacking courage.
19. Without errors, flaws, or faults.

Down

2. Musical keyboard instrument.
3. Occurring at, or existing in, an earlier time.
4. To a greater distance, degree, or extent.
5. With everything included.
7. Every time, for all time, or continually.
8. The state of feeling pleasantly relaxed, or relief from pain.
9. Allow something.
12. Talk on a religious or moral subject.
13. Clothing item.
14. In addition, likewise, or moreover.
16. Kill somebody illegally and deliberately.

Score

Mystery Letter

20

harvest	garment
alarm	farther
perhaps	permit
perfect	sermon

Word Bank
TOTAL
2,340

Exercise 117a

1) The boys bought a _____ to allow them to fish in the lake.

2) The washing had been hung out for several hours and it was _____ dry.

3) _____ he knew which road they lived in, he did not know which house.

4) She saw her friends a bit _____ down the road and ran to catch up with them.

5) He gave a wonderful rendition of Bach's *Toccata and Fugue* on the _____ .

6) The fire _____ sounded and they evacuated the building quickly.

7) The gymnast scored a _____ ten on the parallel bars.

8) He walked past every morning and, without fail, he would _____ wave to her.

9) He was found guilty of _____ and sentenced to life imprisonment.

10) The theme for the vicar's _____ was 'Love thy neighbour'.

Score ⬜ 10

Exercise 117b

11) There are four bedrooms _____ : three upstairs and one downstairs.

12) He ran away and the others called him a _____ .

13) It is a beautiful _____ and she takes great pleasure in wearing it.

14) Workers from neighbouring farms join together to gather in the autumn _____ .

15) The box office had not yet opened but the queue for tickets was _____ long.

16) The newly-elected club captain was introduced by the _____ captain.

17) "It is _____ as much as fifteen miles to the next petrol station."

18) Not only had he lost his shoe, he had _____ lost his sock.

19) It was a nice hotel but she missed the _____ of her own bed.

20) There are both apple and pear trees in the _____ .

Score ⬜ 10

pitch	stitch	kitchen
stretch	cargo	artist
enjoy	enjoyed	tease
weave	preach	beneath

Exercise 118a

1) " _____ ! Can you hear the train coming?"

2) He stood at the _____ sink doing the washing-up.

3) A fine gold thread was _____ into the cloth and it looked exquisite.

4) His mother hoped he would _____ his first day at nursery school.

5) The doctor prescribed antibiotics to _____ her recovery from the infection.

6) They sat in the shade _____ the chestnut tree and ate their picnic.

7) His parents stood beside the football _____ and shouted encouragement.

8) She bought four boxes of six eggs, making two _____ in total.

9) "It's not _____ that you see a total eclipse of the sun."

10) She learned how to _____ baskets at evening classes.

Score ◰ 10

Exercise 118b

11) They stood and watched the _____ paint the girl's portrait.

12) The ship's _____ of food and clothing was being unloaded and put onto lorries.

13) "Don't _____ the dog with that biscuit. Make him sit and then give it to him."

14) Every week, the maids change the bed _____ and clean the apartment.

15) They had not _____ their holiday and were pleased to be going home.

16) The delightful smell of bread baking in the _____ wafted through the house.

17) Married for fifty years, they celebrated their _____ wedding anniversary.

18) He developed a painful _____ in his abdomen and had to stop running.

19) "Don't be a hypocrite; always practise what you _____ !"

20) She really has to _____ up to reach the top shelf.

Score ◰ 10

oven   woven
golden   dozen
linen   often
hasten   listen

Word Bank TOTAL 2,360

Across

2. Give a sermon.
5. A performer, or creator of art.
6. Length of thread in a material for decoration, or to join.
8. Heated cooking compartment.
11. Take pleasure in something.
12. Frequently.
15. To make something by interlacing strands.
16. With a deep, rich, yellow colour or sheen of gold.
17. A room or area where food is prepared and cooked.
19. Extend or become extended.

Down

1. Make fun of somebody.
2. To secure something in the ground, or to set up a temporary structure.
3. Make something happen more quickly.
4. Make a conscious effort to hear.
7. Created by weaving.
9. Benefited from a desirable condition or situation.
10. Group of twelve objects or people.
13. Underneath or lower than.
14. Fabric made from flax.
18. Goods carried as freight.

118

Score / 20

Mystery Letter

cheap   seam   eagle
eager   hotel   camel
label   angel   armour
parlour   colour   favour

Across

119

3. Mean to do something.
5. Meat from the back and side of a pig that has been salted, dried, and often smoked.
6. Desert, ruminant animal with one or two humps.
8. Place for an overnight stay.
10. Protective garment tied around the waist over the front of clothes.
11. Tint, shade or hue.
12. Heavenly being, or a spirit that protects and offers advice.
15. Most liked person or thing.
17. Look at something to judge its quality or correctness.
19. A feeling of curiosity or concern.

Down

1. An act of kindness.
2. Line along which pieces are joined by sewing.
4. A living room set aside for entertaining guests.
7. Anything that gives protection or acts as a safeguard.
9. An informative item attached to something.

Down (continued)

11. Costing little.
13. Take hold of something.
14. A state or people ruled over by a monarch.
16. Large bird of prey.
18. Enthusiastic and excited about doing something.

Mystery Letter   Score

20

© 2006 Stephen Curran

Word Bank
TOTAL
2,380

Exercise 119a

1) They broke their journey and stayed overnight in a _____ .

2) The supermarket had green, smoked, back and streaky _____ on display.

3) Knights wore heavy suits of _____ to protect them in battle.

4) Her job is to _____ the finished vases and to reject any with flaws.

5) A rich _____ of anthracite coal was discovered in the mine.

6) Several aircraft were parked on the _____ in front of the terminal building.

7) It is often a false economy to buy _____ products of inferior quality.

8) "I did _____ to call in and see you but I have been too busy."

9) My sister works as a manicurist in a beauty _____ .

10) The monarch and his queen ruled their _____ .

Score ◿ 10

Exercise 119b

11) Most of the old photographs were monochrome with only a few in _____ .

12) He tried to explain but she could not _____ the implications of her action.

13) Her _____ colour is blue but her brother prefers green.

14) The address _____ came off the parcel and it could not be delivered.

15) She earned a high rate of _____ when she invested the money.

16) She tries very hard never to _____ one of her children more than the others.

17) He was _____ to help and volunteered immediately.

18) The Arabian _____ , or dromedary, has only one hump; the Bactrian has two.

19) "Be an _____ and help me get the washing in."

20) An _____ 's young are called eaglets.

Score ◿ 10

castle	thistle	whistle
whisper	grown	blown
widow	velvet	fare
bare	dare	stare

Exercise 120a

1) The guard waved his flag, blew his _____ and the train pulled away.

2) A deer's antlers shed their furry covering of _____ when they stop growing.

3) The old _____ collapsed in the street and was taken to hospital.

4) The suffragette movement united _____ who campaigned for the right to vote.

5) The referee tossed the coin and the team _____ called, "Tails!"

6) When fully _____ , the giraffe is the tallest living animal.

7) Scotland's national emblem is the _____ .

8) "How _____ you disobey me! Go to your room at once!"

9) After Christmas, the living room looked so _____ without the decorations.

10) Several trees were _____ down during the storm.

Score ⬜ 10

Exercise 120b

11) The Battle of _____ was fought in the skies over south east England in 1940.

12) The waiter assured her that the food did not _____ any nuts.

13) In case of emergency, he carried a _____ inner tube in his pannier bag.

14) It was an amazing spectacle and he continued to _____ wide-eyed.

15) He chose a varnish with a matching colour to _____ and seal the wood.

16) The _____ race has existed on Earth for a relatively short time.

17) Her husband died and she claimed her _____ 's pension.

18) He spoke in a _____ and she could hardly hear his reply.

19) The army laid siege to the well-fortified _____ to force those within to surrender.

20) "How did you _____ in your examinations?"

Score ⬜ 10

10

© 2006 Stephen Curran ae

Word Bank TOTAL 2,400

Across

2. Commander of a boat, aircraft or spacecraft.
3. Country comprising England, Scotland and Wales.
6. A prickly weed.
10. Having developed and matured.
12. A large fortified building.
13. Make a shrill sound through pursed lips.
15. Breathe words voicelessly.
17. Adult female human being.
18. To look directly at something or somebody for a long time.

120

Down (continued)

5. Fabric with a soft lustrous pile.
7. Made up of people.
8. Amount charged for a journey.
9. Moved with a current or air.
11. Plural of 'woman'.
14. Refrain from harming somebody.
15. A woman whose husband has died.
16. A challenge to do something dangerous or frightening.

Down

1. Not covered by clothing, or without decoration.
2. To have something inside, or to hold something.
4. Discoloured mark made by something such as blood, wine or ink.

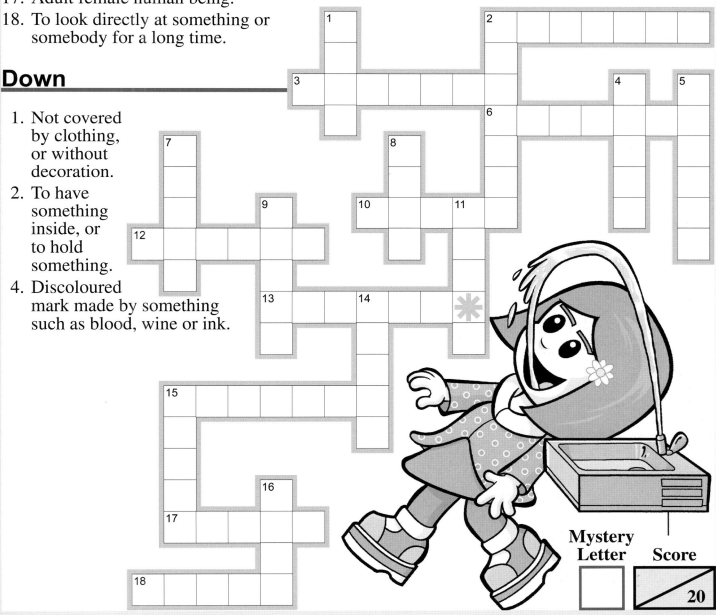

Mystery Letter

Score

20

explain expect express
extent idle island
share pantry fountain
mountain certain extra

Across

121

1. A simple, flat, raised structure.
4. Lazy and unwilling to work.
6. Without doubt.
7. To make the meaning of something clear.
10. Added to, or over and above, the usual, original, or necessary amount.
11. To wait for, or look forward to, an anticipated thing.
12. Land surrounded by water.
15. To have or use something in common with others.

Across (continued)

16. Small room for storing food.
17. Range or scope.
18. Somebody, especially a child, who plays with another.

Down

1. Short, flat-bladed oar.
2. High and often rocky area of land mass with steep or sloping sides.
3. Midway part or position.
5. State thoughts or feelings in words.
6. To impair the ability of something to move.
8. Ornamental water feature.
9. A printed account of news and comment on current affairs.
13. A period of 14 days.
14. Interfere or become involved in someone else's concerns.

Mystery Letter

Score

20

12

paddle　**meddle**
middle　**cripple**
playmate　**newspaper**
platform　**fortnight**

Exercise 121a

1) The saboteur used explosives to damage the rudder and _____ the ship.

2) The train left on time at twelve minutes past eleven from _____ three.

3) "I was away for a _____ but the two weeks rushed by so quickly."

4) My son likes to _____ with my computer and change the settings.

5) He does not speak Italian, so it is difficult for him to _____ what he wants.

6) She bought an _____ loaf of bread as her parents were staying the night.

7) Water gushed from the ornamental _____ .

8) The factory is closed and the machinery is standing _____ .

9) Her usual _____ was absent so she palled up with someone else.

10) The businessman bought one _____ in the company.　**Score** ⟋ 10

Exercise 121b

11) The _____ train roared through the little station without stopping.

12) Last Sunday's _____ came with a colour supplement and a free DVD.

13) My great grandmother's house had a _____ where food was stored.

14) "I didn't _____ to see you here; I thought you weren't coming."

15) She was _____ that she had closed the door but now it was wide open.

16) The dispute continued after the two parties failed to find any _____ ground.

17) Experts were called in after the fire to assess the _____ of the damage.

18) Standing 8,854 metres tall, Mount Everest is the world's highest _____ .

19) Crete is a very picturesque _____ set in the Mediterranean Sea.

20) People like to _____ in the sea at the water's edge.　**Score** ⟋ 10

hoof	smooth	stoop
stooped	settle	midday
midnight	choose	draper
grate	scale	escape

Across

122

3. Metal bars used to keep solid fuel within a fireplace, stove, or furnace.
4. Bony plate on a fish.
8. Decide from among a range of options.
10. A child of somebody's aunt or uncle.
11. Twelve o'clock noon.
12. The life force of an individual.
14. Animal's foot of horny material.
16. The furthest point, degree, amount, or boundary.
18. To solve a problem or end a dispute.
19. Walked or stood bent over.

Down

1. A communication in speech, writing or signals.
2. A seller of fabric and sewing materials.
5. Relating to or concerning people as a whole, or all members of a community.
6. A unit of local government into which England and Wales are divided.
7. A nation or state that is politically independent.
9. Twelve o'clock at night.
12. Without lumps or pieces of solid matter.
13. Demonstrating a lack of courage or self-assurance.
15. Break free from captivity.
17. The downwards swoop of a bird of prey.

Mystery Letter

Score

20

14

© 2006 Stephen Curran

county   country   Word Bank
cousin   message   TOTAL
limit   spirit   2,440
timid   public

Exercise 122a

1) The old man's body had become very _____ and he walked with a stick.

2) He was well known in the community and a respected _____ figure.

3) She asked the waiter to _____ some Parmesan cheese over her pasta.

4) The team played well together and had a real competitive _____ .

5) The blacksmith fashioned a new shoe for the horse's _____ .

6) She was too _____ to go in on her own and so she waited for her friend.

7) It was a beautiful one-tenth _____ model and the detail was amazing.

8) At _____ the sun was almost directly overhead and the heat was intense.

9) There was no wind and the surface of the lake was as _____ as glass.

10) Surrey beat Yorkshire in the _____ cricket competition.   Score [/ 10]

Exercise 122b

11) 'The Black _____' was so called due to the number of coal mines in the area.

12) The 'witching hour' is from _____ until one o'clock in the morning.

13) I checked my voice mail to see if anyone had left a _____ for me.

14) He was summonsed and fined for exceeding the speed _____ in his car.

15) "Take your time and _____ carefully from the options available."

16) She bought the pattern and the fabric to make her dress from the _____ 's shop.

17) They were trapped, with no way to _____ from the sinking ship.

18) He is over two metres tall and has to _____ to go through a doorway.

19) They watched the sediment _____ at the bottom of the flask.

20) Her uncle Frank's son was her _____ .   Score [/ 10]

Wales	Scotland	England
English	laugh	laughed
laughter	linger	lately
safely	nicely	lovely

Exercise 123a

1) _____ 's national anthem is entitled *God Save the Queen*.

2) In Venice, the _____ boats that transport passengers are called *'vaporetti'*.

3) It is said that the monster *'Nessie'* inhabits Loch Ness in _____ .

4) Many regulations ensure that even dangerous work can be carried out _____ .

5) The portrait was a good _____ and captured his features perfectly.

6) "He has been here many times before but I haven't seen him _____ ."

7) Admiral Nelson won a great _____ at the Battle of Trafalgar in 1805.

8) It is very _____ that some form of life exists on another planet.

9) The audience _____ at the comedian's jokes.

10) There are about 350 million native speakers of _____ .   Score [/ 10]

Exercise 123b

11) She seemed reluctant to leave and continued to _____ near the exit.

12) The escape plan had a serious _____ and it was certain to fail.

13) "Mind your table manners: eat your food _____ and don't make a mess!"

14) He was a _____ to their home but they treated him as one of the family.

15) Snowdon is the highest mountain in England and _____ .

16) She wore a _____ outfit, with a wide-brimmed hat, to her daughter's wedding.

17) The sound of children's _____ confirmed that they were enjoying themselves.

18) The police went to the house to _____ her parents of the accident.

19) He sat on his own, apart from the others, and looked very _____ .

20) "Don't _____ at your own jokes."   Score [/ 10]

16

ae

Across

123

5. Lack of strength or determination.
6. Nation to the north of England forming part of Great Britain.
8. People from England.
10. Lacking companionship, aid or encouragement.
11. Not dangerously.
13. Make sounds expressing amusement.
15. Expressed amusement, contempt or disrespect for something.
16. Probable.
18. Defeat of an enemy or opponent.
19. A machine that creates motion.

Down

1. Somebody who visits a person or place.
2. Nation to the west of England forming part of Great Britain.
3. Pleasantly or enjoyably.
4. Beautiful and pleasing.
7. Similarity of appearance.
9. To communicate information or knowledge to somebody.
12. Recently.
13. The sound or an act of laughing.
14. Country that is the largest and most populous of the United Kingdom.
17. To put off leaving because you are reluctant to go.

! Don't forget to go back to page **3** and complete **●** Kate's Mystery Word.

Mystery Letter   **Score**

/ 20

In the Garden

Can you find all these words in the picture below? Write the correct word against each number. When you have finished you can colour in the picture if you want to.

lawnmower	**trellis**	**statue**	**barbecue**	**trowel**
spade	**rake**	**hose**	**logs**	**decking**
fence	**fountain**	**nesting box**	**tulips**	**border**

1._____   2._____   3._____

4._____   5._____   6._____

7._____   8._____   9._____

10._____   11._____   12._____

13._____   14._____   15._____

At the Hairdresser

Can you find all these words in the picture below? Write the correct word against each number.

scissors	crimper	towel	hairdryer	curling tong
gown	reflection	magazine	floor tiles	stylist
receptionist	buckle	locker	bunches	clippers

1._____   2._____   3._____

4._____   5._____   6._____

7._____   8._____   9._____

10._____   11._____   12._____

13._____   14._____   15._____

© 2006 Stephen Curran

servant	merchant	distant
important	though	through
empire	admire	arrive
advice	adventure	nature

Exercise 124a

1) The ship crossed the _____ on its voyage from Mexico to Britain.

2) The _____ ship is carrying a cargo of motor cars.

3) He was _____ that he did not know the answer to such a simple question.

4) They were late, even _____ they had run all the way there.

5) Her letter was stamped and addressed correctly but it failed to _____ .

6) "Listen very carefully: it is very _____ that you pay attention."

7) Scott's final expedition to the South Pole proved to be a fatal _____ .

8) Bill Gates built up his business _____ from very modest beginnings.

9) The system will not _____ anyone without their security pass.

10) The refrigerator kept the food at a _____ temperature.　**Score**　/ 10

Exercise 124b

11) She asked for their _____ and her parents helped her to decide.

12) It was so noisy that he could not shout loud _____ to make himself heard.

13) "Let's meet this _____ at eight o'clock and go to the cinema."

14) Although it seemed unlikely, in the _____ someone came to his rescue.

15) An athlete achieves success _____ rigorous training and endeavour.

16) Her uncle is a civil _____ and works at the Ministry of Defence.

17) This Labrador has a very placid _____ and is very good with children.

18) Today we _____ Florence Nightingale's contribution to medical hygiene.

19) She would _____ herself by doing jigsaw puzzles and reading.

20) He remains very _____ and seems unfriendly.　**Score**　/ 10

constant amuse evening equator admit ashamed event enough

Word Bank TOTAL 2,480

Across
124

5. The physical world.
6. To make somebody smile or laugh.
11. Somebody's opinion about what another person should do.
12. Confess.
13. Far away.
16. Important incident.
17. Lands ruled by a single authority.
18. Past the limitations or difficulties of something.
19. Embarrassed or regretful.
20. And yet, or nevertheless.

Down

1. Somebody who buys and sells goods.
2. Worthy of note or consideration for its interest, value, or relevance.
3. As much as is needed.
4. Always present or available.
7. Imaginary circle around the Earth.
8. To be pleased by, or to respect somebody.
9. Part of the day between afternoon and night as daylight begins to fade.
10. An exciting experience.
14. To reach a place after coming from another place.
15. Somebody employed to do household jobs.

Put the mystery letter (✳) into the box marked **124** below. Add in the mystery letters from puzzles **125** to **130**, then rearrange them to make **Dickens's Mystery Word**. The clue is **BOAT**.

124	125	126	127	128	129	130

Enter your mystery letters here:

Now rearrange them:

Mystery Word:

Score /20

object	subject	robin
holiday	sailor	tailor
railway	daily	rough
tough	rainy	rocky

Exercise 125a

1) The 19th Century was the heyday of the steam _____ system.

2) The table was a bit _____ , so the waiter put a folded serviette under one leg.

3) The river that runs through the _____ is very swollen since the heavy rainfall.

4) Every morning, stable lads take racehorses for a _____ on the downs.

5) His brother is a _____ in the merchant navy and travels the world.

6) It was agreed in principle, _____ to final approval by the committee.

7) _____ camps were at the height of their popularity in the 1950s and 1960s.

8) They offered the _____ of a year's free insurance and servicing with every car.

9) "He has passed a _____ set of exams with top marks."

10) "I _____ to your remarks and insist that you apologise!" **Score** / 10

Exercise 125b

11) The _____ hall is used by the local community for exhibitions and meetings.

12) He has an early morning job delivering the _____ newspapers.

13) The _____ white is a light-coloured butterfly with destructive larvae.

14) The _____ , searching for food in the snow, was distinctive with its red breast.

15) The roof _____ leaked, so the flashing in both of them had to be replaced.

16) The terrain was very _____ and the hikers made slow progress.

17) The forecast is for a _____ day interspersed with very few dry periods.

18) His expensive suit was made by a famous _____ in Savile Row.

19) The house _____ is closely associated with human habitation.

20) She has a sore throat and finds it hard to _____ food. **Score** / 10

Across

125

4. Large areas of low-lying land around a river and its tributaries.
6. Period of time free from work and normal activity and given over to leisure and recreation.
7. Long, low area of land that is surrounded by higher ground.
8. Thin, orange-coloured root vegetable.
10. A small thrush with a reddish-orange breast and forehead.

Across (continued)

13. A small, graceful, swift-flying migratory songbird with long pointed wings and a notched or forked tail.
15. With a lot of rain.
16. Small, dull-coloured songbird.
18. Something that can be seen or touched.
19. Able to withstand much use, strain, or wear without damage.
20. A group of houses and other buildings in a rural area, smaller than a town but larger than a hamlet.

Down

1. Done or occurring every day.
2. Consisting of, or covered with, rocks.
3. Somebody who makes, alters, or repairs clothes.
5. Somebody who works aboard a boat or ship.
9. A track made of rails.
11. The fastest pace of a horse.
12. A matter that is being discussed, examined, or otherwise dealt with.
14. A vegetable with a short stem and a roundish head of closely layered green, white or red leaves.
17. Not smooth or flat.

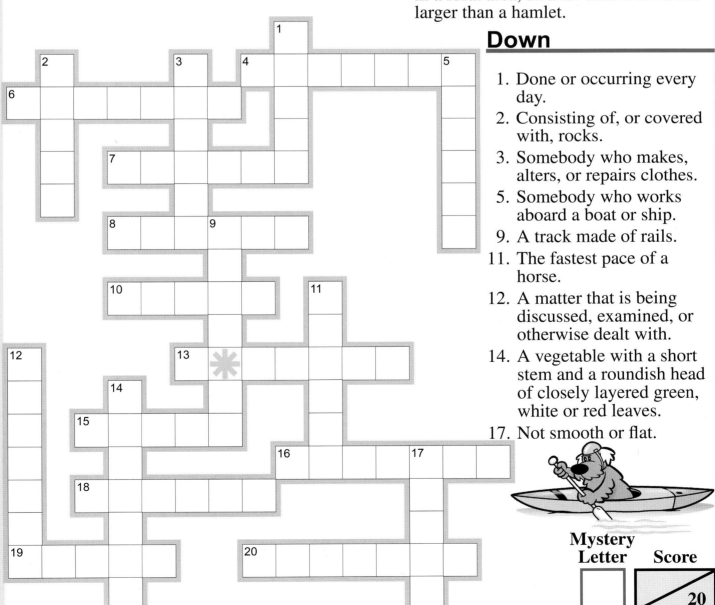

Mystery Letter

Score /20

Across

126

1. A district with its own church.
6. Disappear suddenly or inexplicably.
7. At or on the opposite side of something.
9. To exile somebody from a place.
12. Frayed or torn into irregular shapes or pieces, especially along the edges.
13. To separate and move suddenly in different directions.
14. A room used for work that involves reading, thinking or writing.
16. Took part in a war or battle.

Across (continued)

18. Done in a hurry because of impetuosity or lack of time.
19. Idea produced by a mental activity.

Down

2. In contact with something by leaning or resting on the side of it.
3. Yellow alloy of zinc and copper.
4. Without help from others.
5. Having little natural light.
8. Indicates duty or obligation, probability or expectation, rightness or suitability.
9. Acquired by payment.
10. To die or decay.
11. Came with somebody or something.
15. Showing spitefulness, malice, or ill-nature.
17. In a group, or between group members.

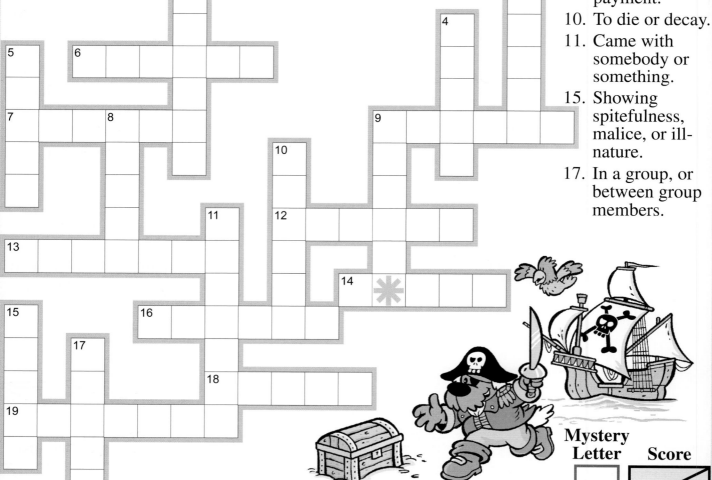

Mystery Letter

Score

20

nasty	hasty
shady	study
vanish	banish
perish	parish

Word Bank TOTAL 2,520

Exercise 126a

1) Father Vincent is the vicar at the villagers' local _____ church.

2) He watched the ship sail away into the distance and _____ over the horizon.

3) The groundsman prepared the soil and then began to _____ the grass seed.

4) They survived the night _____ all the odds and were rescued the next day.

5) It was too damp and _____ under the trees for anything to grow there.

6) She _____ all her groceries at the local supermarket.

7) He had a _____ accident last year and it has taken him all this time to recover.

8) She knew that she _____ not to disobey her parents but this was an emergency.

9) "Leave those jam tarts _____ ; they have just come out of the oven!"

10) They walked single file _____ the narrow bridge.

Score ◸ 10

Exercise 126b

11) The two armies _____ a terrible battle outside the city walls.

12) Drought and severe climate caused many species of the flora and fauna to _____ .

13) Fagin's school for young criminals comprised many _____ street urchins.

14) Working to _____ war and poverty from the world is a noble objective.

15) She divided the cake _____ them by cutting it into six equal portions.

16) "Don't be too _____ ; take all the time you need before you decide."

17) He _____ that he had prepared for every eventuality but this was unexpected.

18) Every colliery had its own _____ band and competition between them was fierce.

19) Several of the children _____ a packed lunch with them.

20) She used a magnifying glass to _____ the map more closely.

Score ◸ 10

25

fancy	ugly	polish
Welsh	lawn	dawn
famous	dangerous	lays
laying	laid	thankful

Exercise 127a

1) "Count yourself lucky and be _____ for small mercies!"

2) The copy is _____ reproduced and includes every original feature.

3) New signs have been erected to warn of the _____ bend.

4) He mowed the _____ and trimmed the edges.

5) They had to wait _____ the sun came up before they could proceed.

6) She was very _____ not to wake her baby when she crept into the room.

7) Tempers frayed, the crowd became violent and things turned very _____ .

8) First he washed his car and then he used a wax _____ to make it shine like new.

9) "He's _____ to come to the telephone; can I take a message?"

10) The fitters are _____ the carpet tomorrow.

Score / 10

Exercise 127b

11) It was a _____ and expressive piece of music with rich harmonies.

12) Many _____ supporters had travelled from Cardiff for the match.

13) _____ broke to reveal that, during the night, a light dusting of snow had fallen.

14) She was so _____ that photographers pursued her wherever she went.

15) A parade through London was organised to _____ home the victorious team.

16) Every time she _____ the baby in his cot and walks away, he begins to cry again.

17) Helen of Troy was reputed to be a woman of outstanding _____ .

18) The theme for the _____ dress party was nursery rhyme characters.

19) The road was icy that day and he drove to work very _____ .

20) Thousands of soldiers have _____ down their lives in battle.

Score / 10

Across

127

3. Make something smooth or shiny by rubbing.
6. With painstaking attention to detail.
7. Up to a time or event but not afterwards.
13. Area of closely mown grass.
14. Likely to cause or result in injury or harm.
16. Pleasing and impressive qualities.
19. Feeling or expressing gratitude.
20. Arranging, placing, or spreading something on, over, or along a surface.

Down

1. In a loyal, true, or accurate way.
2. Very pleasing to the senses, especially to look at.
4. Sets something down, often carefully, in a horizontal position.
5. Received or entertained gladly and generously.
8. Produced eggs.
9. Very well known.
10. Coming from Wales.
11. To want to have or do something.
12. Not able to do something.
15. Acting with caution and attention.
17. Lacking appealing physical features, especially facial ones.
18. The first appearance of light in the sky at the beginning of a new day.

Mystery Letter **Score**

20

glance	advance	distance
France	protect	monster
bough	plough	stumble
grumble	thimble	tremble

Across

128

1. Great joy or pleasure.
6. Very small in size, degree, amount or importance.
9. To look at quickly.
11. A number of things tied, wrapped, or held together.
13. A protective cap for the finger used when sewing.
14. Having high ideals or excellent moral character.
15. Shake slightly but uncontrollably.
17. Stretched so there is no slack.
18. Strong and powerful.
19. Farm implement for breaking up soil and making furrows.

Down

1. The length between two things.
2. Complain or mutter in a discontented way.
3. Continental republic separated from England by the Channel.
4. Move forward in position.
5. To climb or advance over something using both hands and feet.
7. A large, ugly, terrifying creature.
8. To set something alight, or to begin to burn.
10. Keep something or somebody safe.
12. Large main branch of a tree.
16. Trip over when walking or running.

Mystery Letter

Score

20

28

© 2006 Stephen Curran

scramble   bundle

kindle   noble

tight   slight

delight   mighty

Word Bank
TOTAL
2,560

Exercise 128a

1) Her teacher spent time with her in attempt to _____ her interest in the subject.

2) The cross-Channel ferry sails between England and _____ .

3) Pompeii was destroyed in A.D. 79 following a _____ eruption of Vesuvius.

4) He ran from his pursuers at great speed, trying hard not to _____ and fall.

5) He climbed the oak tree and sat astride a _____ in an effort to see further afield.

6) There was only a _____ dent in the car door where the cyclist had hit it.

7) She wears a solid silver _____ that her grandmother used when sewing.

8) The order was given to _____ and the soldiers made their way forward.

9) She was close to tears and her bottom lip began to _____ .

10) He pulled the rope _____ and knotted it securely.

Score ⬜ 10

Exercise 128b

11) There was a _____ for food when supplies for the refugees were unloaded.

12) "To my _____ , I noted that care had been taken to provide for the most needy."

13) He turned to avoid the snowball and he felt it _____ off his left shoulder.

14) She could just make out the church spire far away in the _____ .

15) The legendary Loch Ness _____ has been the subject of many hoaxes.

16) The restaurant made the _____ gesture of giving surplus food to the homeless.

17) Welders wear a visor with very dark glass to _____ their eyes from the glare.

18) She carried a _____ of dirty clothing to the stream where she washed it.

19) The winner was the one who could _____ the straightest furrow.

20) He was very hungry and his stomach began to _____ .

Score ⬜ 10

bucket	trumpet	shrub
liberty	error	terror
ribbon	cotton	Scottish
mutton	blossom	correct

Exercise 129a

1) "He is a very _____ boy who resents being asked to help."

2) Slaves gained their _____ when the slave trade was abolished.

3) He reminded me to _____ my watch and set it to local time before we landed.

4) The boys used a sponge and a _____ of soapy water to wash the car.

5) She added barley, carrots and onions to the _____ stew.

6) She was really afraid and the _____ showed in her eyes.

7) Haggis is a traditional _____ round sausage made from lamb or beef offal.

8) I watched the lion _____ its prey: by staying upwind it remained undetected.

9) The barber stropped the _____ before shaving his customer.

10) She wears contact lenses to _____ her astigmatism.

Score [/10]

Exercise 129b

11) We heard the elephant _____ a warning and then it charged.

12) The fruit trees were covered with _____ that looked and smelled wonderful.

13) The firefighters strove hard to control the _____ but it was a hopeless task.

14) The characters are faint because the printer _____ needs replacing.

15) He would stand in front of the shop window and _____ longingly at the toys.

16) He made a serious _____ of judgement by diving into the pool's shallow end.

17) The _____ has grown too big and woody and needs pruning.

18) Too much _____ in your diet is bad for you and may exacerbate hypertension.

19) She used a _____ bud to apply her make-up.

20) The white cliffs of Dover are composed of _____ .

Score [/10]

chalk   stalk
salt   alter
gaze   blaze
razor   lazy

Word Bank TOTAL 2,580

Across

129

2. Powdery white sedimentary rock.
5. A mass of flowers appearing on a tree or bush.
7. To look for a long time with a fixed stare.
9. Freedom to think or act without being constrained.
12. Tropical or subtropical bush producing soft white downy fibres and oil-rich seeds.
13. Flesh of a fully grown sheep eaten as food.
15. Relating to Scotland, or its people or culture.
17. Instrument with a blade used for shaving.
18. To make changes or become different.
19. Decorative strip of fabric.

Down

1. To burn brightly and fiercely.
3. To remove errors from.
4. Unwilling to work or make an effort.
6. Small white crystals of sodium chloride used to season and preserve food.
8. Cylindrical container used for catching or holding liquids or solids.
10. Something unintentionally done wrong.
11. Brass musical instrument with three valves and a flared bell.
14. Intense or overwhelming fear.
15. Any trunkless woody plant.
16. The main stem of a plant.

Mystery Letter   **Score**

20

31

exceedingly	**aerial**	**perennial**
essential	**grinning**	**planning**
tinned	**skinned**	**planned**
suntanned	**porter**	**briefcase**

Exercise 130a

1) They watched the stunt plane carrying out complex _____ manoeuvres.

2) "Keep _____ the gravy until it comes to the boil."

3) We are having _____ fruit with custard for pudding.

4) Drawings of the proposed building were submitted to the _____ office.

5) He returned from holiday fully rested and looking very _____ .

6) The relentless noise from the party next door was beginning to _____ her.

7) It is _____ that you have a good knowledge of spelling and vocabulary.

8) The _____ large crater was caused by a meteorite crashing to Earth.

9) Her tennis _____ was well-used and needed restringing.

10) He went to buy a paperback from the airport _____ .   Score /10

Exercise 130b

11) The West Highland, Airedale and schnauzer are all breeds of _____ .

12) Graffiti and street litter are _____ problems for local councils to tackle.

13) He left his _____ , which contained very important documents, in the taxi.

14) She made a fruit cake with sultanas, _____ , raisins and glacé cherries.

15) The soldiers returned to their _____ after the long route march.

16) She _____ the tomatoes by blanching them in boiling water.

17) The Thames _____ was constructed to protect London from flooding.

18) The Cheshire cat in *Alice's Adventures in Wonderland* was always _____ .

19) The whole operation was _____ with military precision.

20) She asked the _____ to help her with the suitcases.   Score /10

racket	bookstall	
barrier	stirring	**Word Bank**
currants	terrier	**TOTAL**
barracks	irritate	**2,600**

Across

130

1. To an unusually high degree.
4. A metallic rod or wire for sending and receiving radio waves or microwaves.
7. A structure blocking access.
10. A breed of small, lively dog.
11. Causing an emotional or excited reaction.
13. Gave somebody's skin a brownish colour, or took on such a colour.
15. Packed in a tin can.
17. Small case for carrying books and papers.
18. Working out how to do something.
19. Removed the skin from a fruit or vegetable, or from an animal.
20. Of the highest importance for achieving something.

Down

2. Small, dried, seedless grapes.
3. Somebody employed to carry people's luggage.
5. A stand selling books, magazines and newspapers.
6. Made arrangements to do something.
8. A plant that lasts for more than two growing seasons.
9. To cause annoyance or exasperation.
12. Smiling broadly, usually showing the teeth.
14. A building to accommodate military personnel.
16. A lightweight sports bat with a network of strings.

Don't forget to go back to page **20** and complete **Dickens's Mystery Word**.

Mystery Letter

Score /20

At the Library

Can you find all these words in the picture below? Write the correct word against each number.

photocopier	step	barrier	rafter	moustache
shelves	skirt	terminal	librarian	notices
haversack	counter	desk	cupboard	drawers

1._____ 2._____ 3._____

4._____ 5._____ 6._____

7._____ 8._____ 9._____

10._____ 11._____ 12._____

13._____ 14._____ 15._____

At the Swimming Pool

Can you find all these words in the picture below? Write the correct word against each number. When you have finished you can colour in the picture if you want to.

lifebelt	armband	flume	splash	diving board
lockers	floating	lifeguard	steps	ladder
goggles	diver	towel	puddle	snorkel

1._____   2._____   3._____

4._____   5._____   6._____

7._____   8._____   9._____

10._____   11._____   12._____

13._____   14._____   15._____

Exercise 131a

1) Their _____ were adversely affected by the magnetic field.

2) They were heavily outnumbered, so their leader _____ .

3) Engineers _____ under the Channel to link England with France.

4) The doctor used a _____ to listen to the patient's lungs.

5) The jet climbed steeply into the clouds and _____ from view.

6) It was a _____ explosion and the plume of smoke could be seen for miles.

7) The parliamentary candidate _____ the crowd that had assembled.

8) The aeroplane came to a complete stop and he _____ his seat belt.

9) She is a paraplegic and confined to a _____ .

10) His broken arm was plastered and put in a _____ .

Score / 10

Exercise 131b

11) Further investigations _____ the truth and the culprits were arrested.

12) Thomas Becket was _____ in Canterbury Cathedral in 1170.

13) The _____ on the hotel beds were too soft for his liking.

14) His judgment had been _____ by his previous bad experience.

15) His gun's _____ was empty and he had no more ammunition.

16) "When you didn't reply, I thought something terrible had _____ to you."

17) It was easier and safer to use a _____ than to carry the shopping in baskets.

18) Edmund Hillary and Sherpa Tenzing _____ Mount Everest in 1953.

19) The letters with incorrect _____ were returned.

20) He repaid the money he had _____ from his father.

Score / 10

stethoscope
sling
wheelchair
mattresses

trolley
magazine
addresses
compasses

Word Bank TOTAL 2,620

Across

131

1. A device for drawing circles or measuring distances on a map.
4. Gave up possession of something.
5. Without any covering or protection.
8. Produced, or dug a passageway under an obstruction.
11. A carrying strap attached to something.
13. A chair on wheels used as a way of moving around by somebody who cannot walk.
15. Received money as a loan.
16. Very great in size, force or degree.

Across (continued)

17. Medical instrument used to listen to sounds made by the body.
18. A wheeled cart pushed by hand.
19. Undid something.
20. Wrote directions on an item of mail.

Down

2. Killed somebody illegally.
3. Makes a speech to an audience.
6. Vanished from sight.
7. Large pads on which to sleep.
9. A publication issued at regular intervals.
10. Mastered something difficult to overcome.
12. Having a particular colour.
14. Occurred, or existed by chance.

Put the mystery letter (✱) into the box marked **131** below. Add in the mystery letters from puzzles **132** to **138**, then rearrange them to make **Oliver's Mystery Word**. The clue is **NATIONALITY**.

Enter your mystery letters here:

131	132	133	134	135	136	137	138

Now rearrange them:

Mystery Word:

Score

/20

princesses witnesses businesses
actresses expresses kidnapping
flapping whipping worshipping
mayonnaise marmalade yogurt

Across

132

3. Abduction.
4. A machine that converts mechanical energy into electricity.
7. A board made by gluing and compressing together thin layers of wood.
8. Citrus fruit preserve.
14. Aromatic shrub of the mint family which yields an essential oil containing thymol.
15. Taking part in a religious service.
16. Commercial organisations.
17. Thread, cord or twine binding the end of a rope or cable.
18. Sees something happen.
19. States thoughts or feelings in words.

Down

1. Small, red, cup-shaped fruits made up of tiny juicy globes.
2. Powerful explosive.
5. Yellow fat for spreading and cooking.
6. Moving wings up and down.

Down (continued)

9. Women performers in plays, films or television dramas.
10. Milk product fermented by bacteria.
11. Creamy sauce made from egg yolks.
12. Vegetable plant related to the cabbage that has a large solid head of edible white flowers.
13. Monarch's daughters.
15. Edible nuts which have a deeply wrinkled surface.

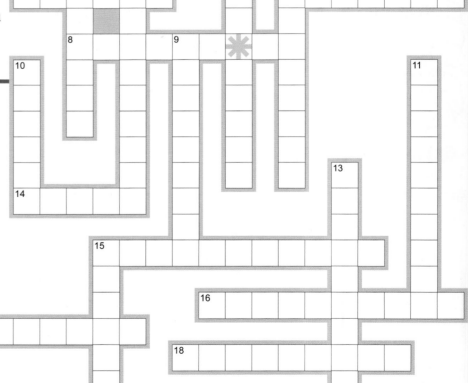

Mystery Letter

Score

20

38

© 2006 Stephen Curran

cauliflower	raspberries
walnuts	margarine
dynamo	dynamite
plywood	thyme

Word Bank TOTAL 2,640

Exercise 132a

1) When cooking, she uses _____ instead of butter.

2) He asked for garlic _____ to put on his jacket potato.

3) A _____ , driven by the front wheel, powers the bicycle's lights.

4) Many _____ auditioned for the role of leading lady.

5) The _____ Elizabeth and Margaret were the children of King George VI.

6) It is a beautiful motor launch with a hull made of _____ .

7) The swan was defending its young by _____ its wings and hissing menacingly.

8) The practice of _____ idols is followed by some religions.

9) Many _____ fail and go into liquidation each year.

10) _____ is used in quarries for blasting rock.

Score / 10

Exercise 132b

11) He was arrested for _____ their daughter and demanding a ransom.

12) She laid sprigs of _____ on the joint to flavour the roast lamb.

13) _____ cheese is a tasty dish and suitable for vegetarians to eat.

14) She _____ the juice from the limes by squeezing them with her fingers.

15) *Yoghurt* is of Turkish origin and may also be spelled as *yoghourt* or _____ .

16) He could shell _____ by squeezing two together in his hand.

17) She preferred coarse cut Seville orange _____ on her toast.

18) It is the high proportion of butterfat in _____ cream that makes it stiffen.

19) The police appealed for _____ to the crime to come forward.

20) She made a coulis from fresh, sweet _____ .

Score / 10

hygiene	hydrogen	hyacinths
python	dynamic	cyclone
hydroelectricity	generously	dangerously
seriously	thoroughly	vertically

Exercise 133a

1) Water has two atoms of _____ and one atom of oxygen.

2) The _____ spread his magnificent green and turquoise tail feathers.

3) A powerful _____ indicates that violent winds and storms are imminent.

4) She revised _____ for the exams and her efforts were rewarded.

5) _____ provides environmentally friendly power.

6) It is important to measure _____ before cutting anything to size.

7) A _____ can grow to over five metres and suffocates its prey by constriction.

8) It is customary for the monarch and the heir to the throne to travel _____ .

9) The public gave _____ to provide aid for the victims of the disaster.

10) Basic rules of _____ prevent the spread of infection.

Score ⊠ 10

Exercise 133b

11) The _____ family comprised a duck, a drake and five ducklings.

12) The police took the threat _____ and cleared the hall as a precaution.

13) _____ , also called 'jacinths', are native to the northeast Mediterranean.

14) Rain was forecast and, very _____ , she took her umbrella.

15) He was acting very _____ and his behaviour worried his friends.

16) The rocket rose _____ , then seemed to lose power and fall to the ground.

17) Events are very _____ and the circumstances could suddenly change.

18) "If you ride your bike _____ , you are likely to have an accident."

19) The sauce is very _____ flavoured, with just a hint of vanilla.

20) She sobbed _____ , feeling desperately sad and lonely.

Score ⊠ 10

ae

miserably	wisely
accurately	delicately
strangely	separately
mallard	peacock

Word Bank TOTAL 2,660

Across

2. Large constricting snake.
5. Standing or moving at a right angle to the horizon.
10. In a subtle, gentle, careful, or tactful way.
11. In an unusual or puzzling way.
14. In a manner of giving readily to others.
16. A wild duck.
17. The lightest and the most abundant gaseous element in the universe.
18. Very unhappily.
19. Lilies with spikes of highly fragrant flowers.

133

Down

1. In a grave and thoughtful way.
3. The science dealing with the preservation of health.
4. Correctly and in an error-free way.
6. Extremely carefully and accurately.
7 A vainglorious person.
8. Electricity produced by water power.
9. Large-scale storm system.
10. In a way that is likely to cause or result in harm or injury.
12. Knowingly, sensibly, or shrewdly.
13. In a non-touching, unconnected, unrelated, or distinct way.
15. Vigorous and purposeful.

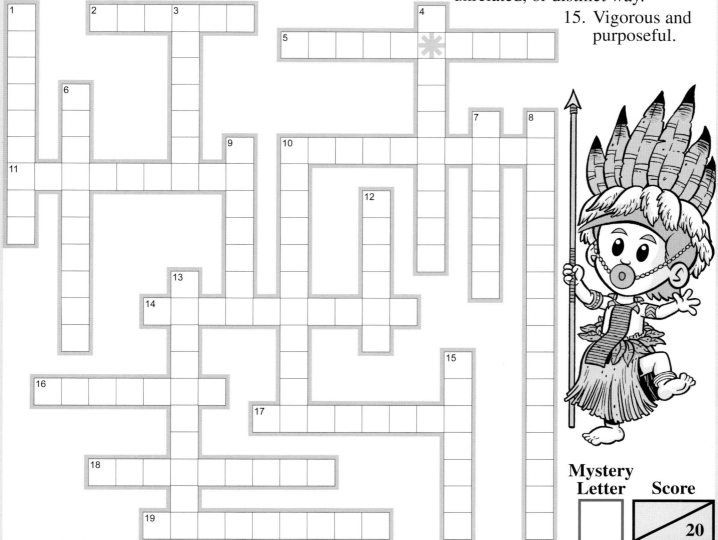

Mystery Letter   **Score**

20

jaguar collide rebellion sparkling

dollar quarrelled aching escaping

poplar signalled surprising examining

Across

(134)

2. Taking, bringing, or carrying goods into a country illegally.
4. Engaged in an angry dispute.
5. Common unit of currency.
10. Leaking out from a container.
13. Inspecting, studying, or investigating in detail.
17. Organised attempt to overthrow a government or other authority.
18. Feeling pain or yearning.
19. Communicated or indicated something.
20. Taking somebody by unawares.

Down

1. Reflecting or giving off light in brilliant glittering flashes.
3. Giving emphasis or extra force to something.
6. Showing great happiness about something.
7. Secreting sweat.
8. Repeating sounds caused by the reflection of sound waves from a surface.
9. A small, slender, biting fly.
11. Declaring a decision or intention not to do or not to accept something.
12. Large cat related to the leopard.
14. Accepting as true.
15. Crash into something.
16. Slender, quick-growing tree of the willow family.

Mystery Letter

Score

20

Exercise 134a

1) A _____ has a tawny coat with black spots inside black rings.

2) Malaria is caused by a parasite transmitted through _____ bites.

3) _____ him now was impossible because he had lied so often before.

4) She was so unhappy and _____ for her mother to be there to comfort her.

5) The television report showed his happy parents _____ at his safe return.

6) Nelson _____ to his fleet: "England expects that every man will do his duty."

7) The concert ends and the auditorium _____ to the sound of applause.

8) Although they had _____ , they made up and remained good friends.

9) They were working under a hot sun and _____ profusely.

10) The American _____ is a worldwide currency.

Score [/10]

Exercise 134b

11) Many men and women have been martyred for _____ to renounce their faith.

12) It is _____ how often he succeeds when the odds are stacked against him.

13) She spent an hour _____ important words and phrases in the text.

14) The prisoners were chained together to prevent them from _____ .

15) After _____ her thoroughly, the consultant diagnosed her illness.

16) A line of _____ trees grew along the hilltop to give protection against the wind.

17) Customs officers at ports and airports deter travellers from _____ .

18) "Look how the water's surface is _____ in the sunlight."

19) The Jacobite _____ was finally defeated at Culloden in 1746.

20) He saw the car skid on the ice and _____ with the bus.

Score [/10]

ae © 2006 Stephen Curran

43

buffaloes	mosquitoes	volcanoes
dominoes	battery	brewery
millinery	stationery	cemetery
artillery	confectionery	colleague

Exercise 135a

1) The pungent smell of hops being boiled at the local _____ hangs in the air.

2) The _____ was the most popular creature on display at the aquarium.

3) His alarm clock had stopped and he had to change the _____ .

4) An ornate _____ decorated with sculpted figures adorned the building.

5) She studied the headstone on her grandfather's grave in the local _____ .

6) _____ are very unpredictable and liable to erupt with little or no warning.

7) On Remembrance Sunday, everyone gathered at the Cenotaph wears a _____ .

8) _____ spread diseases such as malaria, yellow fever and dengue.

9) It is a complex plot, full of mystery, _____ and suspense.

10) She laid her baby on the mat and changed its soiled _____ . **Score** ⟋ 10

Exercise 135b

11) It is an old-fashioned _____ shop that stocks sweets in glass jars.

12) The kennel's champion Border collie _____ gave birth to five puppies.

13) Her work _____ telephoned to say he was sick and would be not be in.

14) All the lights began to _____ , then went out completely when the power failed.

15) In *Twenty Thousand Leagues under the Sea*, a giant _____ attacks the *Nautilus*.

16) North American _____ were hunted almost to extinction.

17) He ordered a further supply of company _____ from the local printer.

18) "Look at your _____ . If you have a double six, you can start the game."

19) He had a _____ business designing and selling women's hats.

20) When the enemy were in range, the _____ opened fire. **Score** ⟋ 10

Across

135

4. Small, oblong tiles either blank or marked with a number of spots.
8. Plant with large red, orange, or white flower and cup-shaped seed pod.
9. A decorative band along the wall of a room, usually just below the ceiling.
10. An area of ground in which the dead are buried.
12. Female dog.
16. Secret scheming or plotting.
17. To burn or shine unsteadily.
18. Heavy-calibre, powerful weapons.
19. Large ocean fish with an upper jaw that extends into a long point.
20. Paper, envelopes, pens, pencils and other things used in writing.

Down

1. A fellow worker.
2. Hats and other accessories for women.
3. More than one mosquito.
5. A marine cephalopod mollusc that has two long tentacles and eight shorter arms.
6. Grouping of similar artillery pieces.

Down (continued)

7. Sweets, or the skill, technique, or practice of making sweets.
11. Plural of 'buffalo'.
13. Company or place where beer is brewed.
14. Naturally occurring openings in the Earth's crust through which molten, gaseous and solid material is ejected.
15. An absorbent towel round baby's bottom.

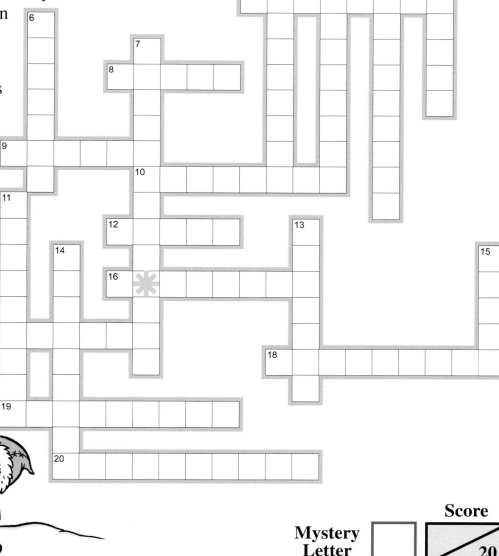

Mystery Letter

Score

/20

fuss	tweed	gerbil
dragon	fleece	pant
itch	jagged	scan
tripped	bypass	squabble

Across

136

1. A road built around a town or city to keep through traffic away from the centre.
4. A trailing plant of the rose family that has white flowers and is cultivated for its edible red fruit.
7. To take short, fast, shallow breaths.
8. A fairly rough, thick, woollen fabric used for warm clothing.

Across (continued)

10. Stumbled or fell as a result of catching the foot on something.
11. To look through or read something quickly.
14. Having sharp protruding parts or points.
16. Needless or excessively busy, or excited activity.
17. Small rodent resembling a mouse with long back legs.
19. A tool, machine, or part of a machine that is used for excavation.

Down

2. A confused jostle or struggle.
3. To have, produce, or cause somebody to feel the desire to scratch.
5. A sudden strong current of air or wind.
6. An adult male goose.
8. Two people or animals born to the same mother at the same time.
9. The woolly coat of a sheep or similar animal.
12. The act of reaching, touching, or alighting on the ground.
13. A noisy argument over a petty matter.
15. A large and usually ferocious fire-breathing creature in myths, legends and fairy tales.
18. An ill-mannered, aggressive, or awkward man or youth.

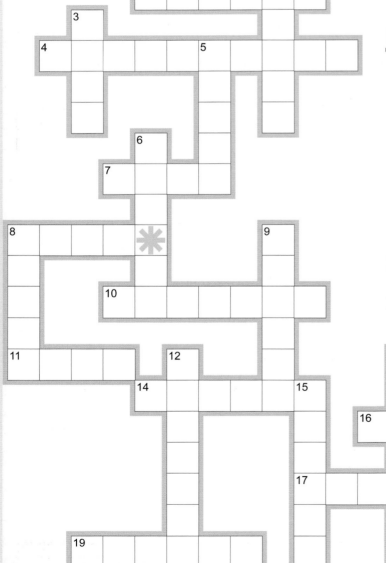

Mystery Letter   Score

20

46

landing   twins

lout   digger

gander   scrum

blast   strawberry

Word Bank
TOTAL
2,720

Exercise 136a

1) Her dog fetched the ball, raced back, sat at her feet and began to _____ breathlessly.

2) The house was destroyed in the _____ caused by the huge gas explosion.

3) "What's all the _____ about? It's only a small problem and easily overcome."

4) The boys continued to _____ rather than play quietly together.

5) The surgeon used a grafted blood vessel to _____ his patient's blocked artery.

6) _____ rocks protrude above the water line and pose a threat to mariners.

7) A mechanical _____ was used to excavate the foundations for the new building.

8) She reached the _____ and then turned to look back down the stairs.

9) The nettle sting began to _____ but applying the dock leaf relieved it.

10) "What's sauce for the goose is sauce for the _____ ."

Score / 10

Exercise 136b

11) The doctor sent her for a _____ to obtain detailed images of her brain.

12) People often find it very difficult to distinguish between identical _____ .

13) The _____ is a small, desert-dwelling rodent that can be kept as a pet.

14) It was very cold outside, so he wore a jumper, a _____ *and* a jacket.

15) The circuit developed a fault, but the relay _____ and switched off the power.

16) The country squire wore a thick, brown _____ suit and a pair of heavy brogues.

17) The sale began and a _____ of frantic customers fought for bargains.

18) "See that horse with a reddish-white coat? It's a _____ roan."

19) According to legend, St. George fought a _____ .

20) "Some oafish _____ pushed past my wife and then swore at her." **Score** / 10

---

vandal	scrub	sweep
twitch	quiz	squash
playful	squeak	quack
pouch	puppet	effort

Exercise 137a

1) Detective Sergeant Bailey continued to _____ the suspect about the crime.

2) The immunisation programme has resulted in far _____ cases occurring today.

3) Every seaside town used to have a *Punch and Judy* _____ show for the children.

4) Young marsupials are usually carried in a _____ on the female's abdomen.

5) Until it was oiled, the hinge used to _____ every time the door was opened.

6) He claimed to be a doctor but, with no formal training, he was just a _____ .

7) It was _____ that, when she retired, her replacement came from her old school.

8) Orange _____ has to be diluted with water before drinking.

9) During the night, a _____ had covered the wall with graffiti.

10) "Fetch the broom and _____ up the mess you have made!" **Score** [/10]

Exercise 137b

11) Their new puppy is very _____ and loves to chase them round the garden.

12) She is very tall and always buys shoes with the _____ heel she can find.

13) The wardrobe is too wide and will not _____ into the alcove in the bedroom.

14) He made a final, desperate _____ and managed to haul himself out of the water.

15) Leather is made by _____ animal hides in solutions containing tannin.

16) She _____ her arm last week and it still looks slightly discoloured.

17) "The ground slopes too much: a football pitch needs a _____ surface."

18) The muscle went into spasm causing his upper cheek to _____ .

19) The outback in Australia is a wilderness where only _____ can grow.

20) They all collapsed into _____ of uncontrollable laughter. **Score** [/10]

Word Bank TOTAL 2,740

Across

137

2. Fond of having fun and playing games with others.
5. To compliment somebody too much, often without sincerity, in order to gain advantage.
7. Most level, most smooth, or least curved.
10. A test of knowledge in the form of a rapid series of questions.
11. Soaking something, or being soaked, in a liquid.
13. The harsh sound typically made by a duck.
14. Clean by rubbing hard.

Across (continued)

16. A small, soft bag or container.
17. Clean a place with a broom.

Down

1. Somebody who maliciously and deliberately defaces or destroys property.
3. Sudden violent convulsions.
4. Installs something, or puts something in place.
5. An even more limited or exclusive number.
6. Mental or physical energy that is exerted in order to achieve a purpose.
7. Suitable, or being in accordance with something.
8. To move with a slight jerk.
9. To make a short, high-pitched sound or cry.
11. To flatten something with pressure.
12. A doll or figure representing a person or animal that is moved using the hands.
15. Hurt and upset, especially as a result of something that has damaged your self-esteem.

Mystery Letter

Score

20

flawed	**cleaner**	**stepped**
fruitful	**tawny**	**fruity**
wrench	**gopher**	**counting**
guy	**halfway**	**cruises**

Exercise 138a

1) We made a _____ from old clothes filled with leaves and burned it on the bonfire.

2) With the increased rainfall, this month is _____ than the same month last year.

3) It was a terrible _____ to leave after having lived in the house for forty years.

4) We stood on the quayside and watched the _____ return with its catch.

5) The carpet looked much _____ after it had been professionally shampooed.

6) This route is _____ but the longer one is much more interesting.

7) Many important facts are not included and the report is seriously _____ .

8) "I am _____ on your support in the forthcoming elections."

9) As the sun rose higher in the sky, the day became even _____ .

10) A jet aircraft _____ at an altitude of over 30,000 feet.   **Score** [/ 10]

Exercise 138b

11) Meat, fish or vegetable _____ are cooked in highly spiced sauces.

12) The genealogist's search was very _____ and identified many ancestors.

13) The American _____ and the Eurasian hamster both have cheek pouches.

14) Although a tomato looks _____ and grows on a plant, it is in fact a vegetable.

15) An ungulate is an animal, such as the deer, cow and horse, that has _____ .

16) They reached the _____ point and later, after a rest, they began their descent.

17) Ebony, whose Latin name *Ebonus* means stone, is the _____ of all the woods.

18) The crowd that had gathered _____ aside to make way for the paramedics.

19) They were over _____ there and still well ahead of schedule.

20) The _____ owl is also known as the *'wood owl'*.   **Score** [/ 10]

Word Bank

hardest
curries
shorter
hotter

trawler
highest
hooves
wetter

Word Bank TOTAL 2,760

Across

138

5. Grooms a horse.
6. Something arranged or organised in steps.
7. A man.
10. Journeys by ship for pleasure.
12. At or to the middle point between two things in space or time.
14. A chemical or machine used for cleaning.
15. Rich and resonant in voice tone.

Across (continued)

16. A small, burrowing rodent of North and Central America.
19. Including or taking a particular person or thing into consideration in a total.
20. The most difficult or awkward to do or achieve.

Down

1. At a relatively higher temperature.
2. Highly productive or creative.
3. Relatively more covered, more soaked, or more dampened with water or some other liquid.
4. Situated in a position above everybody or everything else referred to.
8. Of an orange-brown colour tinged with gold.
9. A boat that is used in trawling for fish.
11. Having less or relatively less length.
13. To pull something away forcefully, often using a twisting movement.
17. Plural of 'hoof'.
18. Imperfect or defective.

❗ Don't forget to go back to page **37** and complete ● **Oliver's Mystery Word.**

Mystery Letter

Score

20

ae © 2006 Stephen Curran

51

Book Six Word List

absent	blanket	consist	enjoyed
accurately	blast	constant	enough
aching	blaze	contain	equator
across	blossom	correct	error
actresses	blown	cotton	escape
addressed	bookstall	counting	escaping
addresses	borrowed	country	essential
admire	bough	county	evening
admit	bought	cousin	event
advance	brass	coward	examining
advantage	brewery	cripple	exceedingly
adventure	briefcase	cruises	expect
advice	Britain	currants	explain
aerial	brought	curries	express
against	bruised	curtain	expresses
alarm	bucket	cyclone	extent
almost	buffaloes	daily	extra
alone	bundle	damage	faithfully
already	businesses	dangerous	famous
also	bypass	dangerously	fancy
alter	cabbage	dare	fare
although	camel	dawn	farther
altogether	captain	delicately	favour
always	careful	delight	favourite
among	carefully	digger	fewer
amuse	cargo	disappeared	fit
angel	carrot	distance	fits
apron	castle	distant	fitting
armour	cauliflower	dollar	flapping
arrive	cemetery	dominoes	flatter
artillery	certain	dozen	flattest
artist	chalk	dragon	flawed
ashamed	cheap	draper	fleece
bacon	choose	dynamic	flicker
banish	cleaner	dynamite	former
bare	colleague	dynamo	fortnight
barracks	collide	eager	fought
barrier	colour	eagle	fountain
battery	coloured	echoes	France
beautiful	comfort	effort	frieze
beauty	compasses	empire	fruitful
believing	conduct	England	fruity
beneath	confectionery	English	furnish
bitch	conquered	enjoy	fuss

Book Six Word List

gallop	kidnapping	mountain	princesses
gander	kindle	murder	proper
garment	kingdom	murdered	property
gaze	kitchen	mutton	protect
generously	label	nappy	public
gerbil	laid	nasty	puppet
glance	landing	nature	purple
golden	lately	newspaper	python
gopher	laugh	nicely	quack
grasp	laughed	noble	quarrelled
grate	laughter	object	quiz
grinning	lawn	often	racket
grown	laying	orchard	ragged
grumble	lays	organ	railway
guy	lazy	ought	rainy
halfway	liberty	oven	raspberries
happened	likely	paddle	razor
hardest	likeness	pant	rebellion
harvest	limit	pantry	refusing
hasten	linen	parent	rejoicing
hasty	linger	parish	remarkable
highest	listen	parlour	ribbon
holiday	lonely	peacock	robin
hoof	lout	perennial	rocky
hooves	lovely	perfect	rough
hotel	magazine	perhaps	safely
hotter	mallard	perish	sailor
human	margarine	permit	salt
hyacinths	marmalade	perspiring	Saturday
hydroelectricity	mattresses	pitch	scale
hydrogen	mayonnaise	planned	scan
hygiene	meddle	planning	scatter
idle	merchant	platform	Scotland
important	message	playful	Scottish
inform	midday	playmate	scramble
inspect	middle	plough	scrub
intend	midnight	plywood	scrum
interest	mighty	polish	seam
intrigue	millinery	poplar	separately
irritate	miserably	poppy	seriously
island	monster	porter	sermon
itch	mosquito	pouch	serpent
jagged	mosquitoes	preach	servant
jaguar	motor	prevent	settle

Book Six Word List

shady	stirring	thought	vertically
share	stitch	through	victory
shorter	stoop	thyme	village
shrub	stooped	tight	visitor
signalled	strangely	timid	volcanoes
silence	strawberry	tinned	voyage
silent	stretch	tough	wages
skinned	study	trawler	Wales
slight	stumble	tremble	walnuts
sling	subject	tripped	weakness
smooth	suntanned	trolley	weave
smuggling	surprising	trumpet	welcome
spare	surrendered	tunnelled	Welsh
sparkling	swallow	tweed	wetter
sparrow	sweep	twins	wheelchair
spirit	swordfish	twitch	whipping
squabble	tailor	ugly	whisper
squash	tawny	unable	whistle
squeak	tease	uncovered	widow
squid	terrier	underlining	wisely
stain	terrific	unfastened	witnesses
stalk	terror	until	woman
stare	thankful	valley	women
stationery	thimble	valleys	worshipping
steeping	thistle	vandal	woven
stepped	thoroughly	vanish	wrench
stethoscope	though	velvet	yogurt

Congratulations!

You have now learnt to spell **2,760** words, know what they mean and how to use them in a sentence.

Now move on to **Book 7** to learn lots more words to add to your word bank total.

Answers

Exercise 116a

1) wages
2) serpent
3) curtain
4) property
5) voyage
6) damage
7) blanket
8) silence
9) Saturday
10) parent

Exercise 116b

11) remarkable
12) purple
13) advantage
14) proper
15) conduct
16) furnish
17) consist
18) silent
19) absent
20) prevent

Crossword No. 116

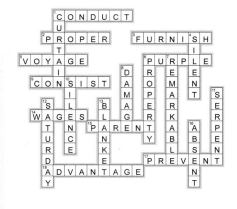

Letter = N

Exercise 117a

1) permit
2) almost
3) Although
4) farther
5) organ
6) alarm
7) perfect
8) always
9) murder
10) sermon

Exercise 117b

11) altogether
12) coward
13) garment
14) harvest
15) already
16) former
17) perhaps
18) also
19) comfort
20) orchard

Crossword No. 117

Letter = D

Exercise 118a

1) Listen
2) kitchen
3) woven
4) enjoy
5) hasten
6) beneath
7) pitch
8) dozen
9) often
10) weave

Exercise 118b

11) artist
12) cargo
13) tease
14) linen
15) enjoyed
16) oven
17) golden
18) stitch
19) preach
20) stretch

Crossword No. 118

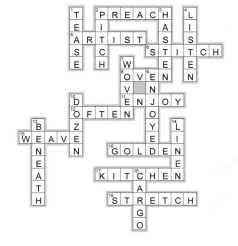

Letter = E

Answers

Exercise 119a
1) hotel
2) bacon
3) armour
4) inspect
5) seam
6) apron
7) cheap
8) intend
9) parlour
10) kingdom

Exercise 119b
11) colour
12) grasp
13) favourite
14) label
15) interest
16) favour
17) eager
18) camel
19) angel
20) eagle

Exercise 120a
1) whistle
2) velvet
3) woman
4) women
5) captain
6) grown
7) thistle
8) dare
9) bare
10) blown

Exercise 120b
11) Britain
12) contain
13) spare
14) stare
15) stain
16) human
17) widow
18) whisper
19) castle
20) fare

Exercise 121a
1) cripple
2) platform
3) fortnight
4) meddle
5) explain
6) extra
7) fountain
8) idle
9) playmate
10) share

Exercise 121b
11) express
12) newspaper
13) pantry
14) expect
15) certain
16) middle
17) extent
18) mountain
19) island
20) paddle

Crossword No. 119

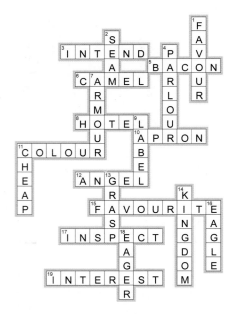

Letter = L

Crossword No. 120

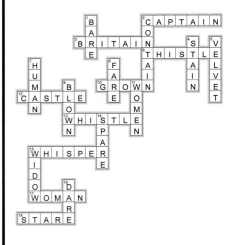

Letter = E

Crossword No. 121

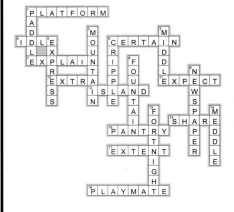

Letter = A

Answers

Exercise 122a
1) stooped
2) public
3) grate
4) spirit
5) hoof
6) timid
7) scale
8) midday
9) smooth
10) county

Exercise 122b
11) Country
12) midnight
13) message
14) limit
15) choose
16) draper
17) escape
18) stoop
19) settle
20) cousin

Exercise 123a
1) England
2) motor
3) Scotland
4) safely
5) likeness
6) lately
7) victory
8) likely
9) laughed
10) English

Exercise 123b
11) linger
12) weakness
13) nicely
14) visitor
15) Wales
16) lovely
17) laughter
18) inform
19) lonely
20) laugh

Exercise 124a
1) equator
2) merchant
3) ashamed
4) though
5) arrive
6) important
7) adventure
8) empire
9) admit
10) constant

Exercise 124b
11) advice
12) enough
13) evening
14) event
15) through
16) servant
17) nature
18) admire
19) amuse
20) distant

Crossword No. 122

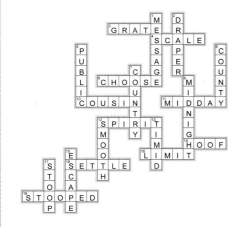

Letter = O

Crossword No. 123

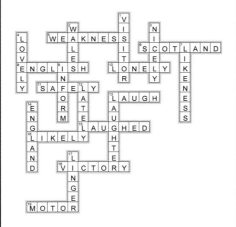

Letter = M

Crossword No. 124

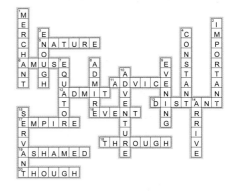

Letter = R

In the Garden

1. BARBECUE	2. TRELLIS	3. RAKE	4. FENCE	5. STATUE
6. NESTING BOX	7. TROWEL	8. DECKING	9. FOUNTAIN	10. BORDER
11. LOGS	12. HOSE	13. SPADE	14. TULIPS	15. LAWNMOWER

At the Hairdresser

1. CURLING TONG	2. BUNCHES	3. STYLIST	4. MAGAZINE	5. RECEPTIONIST
6. BUCKLE	7. REFLECTION	8. GOWN	9. SCISSORS	10. CRIMPER
11. FLOOR TILES	12. LOCKER	13. TOWEL	14. HAIRDRYER	15. CLIPPERS

Answers

Exercise 125a

1) railway
2) rocky
3) valley
4) gallop
5) sailor
6) subject
7) Holiday
8) carrot
9) tough
10) object

Exercise 125b

11) village
12) daily
13) cabbage
14) robin
15) valleys
16) rough
17) rainy
18) tailor
19) sparrow
20) swallow

Crossword No. 125

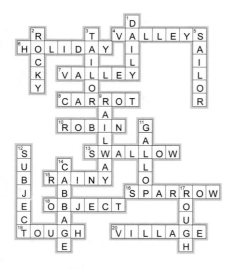

Letter = W

Exercise 126a

1) parish
2) vanish
3) scatter
4) against
5) shady
6) bought
7) nasty
8) ought
9) alone
10) across

Exercise 126b

11) fought
12) perish
13) ragged
14) banish
15) among
16) hasty
17) thought
18) brass
19) brought
20) study

Crossword No. 126

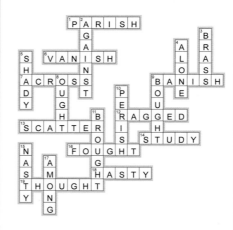

Letter = T

Exercise 127a

1) thankful
2) faithfully
3) dangerous
4) lawn
5) until
6) careful
7) ugly
8) polish
9) unable
10) laying

Exercise 127b

11) beautiful
12) Welsh
13) Dawn
14) famous
15) welcome
16) lays
17) beauty
18) fancy
19) carefully
20) laid

Crossword No. 127

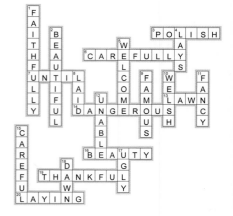

Letter = L

Answers

Exercise 128a

1) kindle
2) France
3) mighty
4) stumble
5) bough
6) slight
7) thimble
8) advance
9) tremble
10) tight

Exercise 128b

11) scramble
12) delight
13) glance
14) distance
15) monster
16) noble
17) protect
18) bundle
19) plough
20) grumble

Exercise 129a

1) lazy
2) liberty
3) alter
4) bucket
5) mutton
6) terror
7) Scottish
8) stalk
9) razor
10) correct

Exercise 129b

11) trumpet
12) blossom
13) blaze
14) ribbon
15) gaze
16) error
17) shrub
18) salt
19) cotton
20) chalk

Exercise 130a

1) aerial
2) stirring
3) tinned
4) planning
5) suntanned
6) irritate
7) essential
8) exceedingly
9) racket
10) bookstall

Exercise 130b

11) terrier
12) perennial
13) briefcase
14) currants
15) barracks
16) skinned
17) barrier
18) grinning
19) planned
20) porter

Crossword No. 128

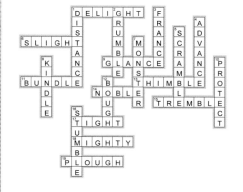

Letter = E

Crossword No. 129

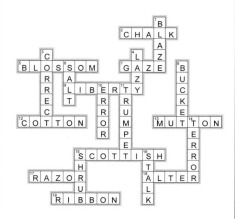

Letter = A

Crossword No. 130

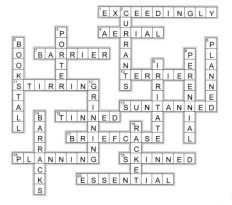

Letter = R

At the Library

1. NOTICES	2. RAFTER	3. SHELVES	4. CUPBOARD	5. MOUSTACHE
6. SKIRT	7. STEP	8. TERMINAL	9. HAVERSACK	10. DESK
11. DRAWERS	12. COUNTER	13. PHOTOCOPIER	14. BARRIER	15. LIBRARIAN

At the Swimming Pool

1. LIFEGUARD	2. SNORKEL	3. FLOATING	4. TOWEL	5. DIVER
6. FLUME	7. PUDDLE	8. LOCKERS	9. GOGGLES	10. LIFEBELT
11. ARMBAND	12. STEPS	13. DIVING BOARD	14. LADDER	15. SPLASH

Answers

Exercise 131a
1) compasses
2) surrendered
3) tunnelled
4) stethoscope
5) disappeared
6) terrific
7) addressed
8) unfastened
9) wheelchair
10) sling

Exercise 131b
11) uncovered
12) murdered
13) mattresses
14) coloured
15) magazine
16) happened
17) trolley
18) conquered
19) addresses
20) borrowed

Exercise 132a
1) margarine
2) mayonnaise
3) dynamo
4) actresses
5) princesses
6) plywood
7) flapping
8) worshipping
9) businesses
10) Dynamite

Exercise 132b
11) kidnapping
12) thyme
13) Cauliflower
14) expresses
15) yogurt
16) walnuts
17) marmalade
18) whipping
10) witnesses
20) raspberries

Exercise 133a
1) hydrogen
2) peacock
3) cyclone
4) thoroughly
5) Hydroelectricity
6) accurately
7) python
8) separately
9) generously
10) hygiene

Exercise 133b
11) mallard
12) seriously
13) Hyacinths
14) wisely
15) strangely
16) vertically
17) dynamic
18) dangerously
19) delicately
20) miserably

Crossword No. 131

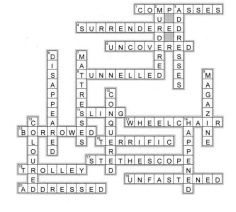

Letter = I

Crossword No. 132

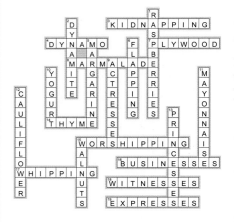

Letter = A

Crossword No. 133

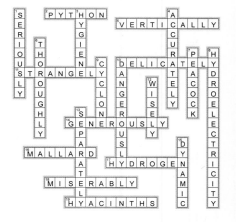

Letter = C